THE POETRY OF BORON

The Poetry of Boron

Walter the Educator™

SKB

Silent King Books a WhichHead Imprint

"Earning a degree in chemistry changed my life!"
– Walter the Educator

dedicated to all the chemistry lovers, like myself, across the world

CONTENTS

WHY I CREATED THIS BOOK?

Creating a poetry book about the chemistry element of Boron was a unique and fascinating endeavor. Boron, with its atomic number 5, is a versatile and interesting element that holds various scientific and poetic possibilities. By exploring its properties, history, and applications, this poetry book about Boron can bridge the gap between science and art, appealing to both science enthusiasts and poetry lovers. This book delves into the beauty of Boron's atomic structure, its role in the natural world, and its significance in human life, resulting in a collection that celebrates the wonders of science in a creative and imaginative way.

ONE

CELEBRATE BORON

In the realm of elements, Boron stands bold,
A chemical marvel, with stories untold.
Symbolized by B, it holds secrets within,
A fascinating element, where wonders begin.
With an atomic number of five, it resides,
In the periodic table, where knowledge presides.
A metalloid it is, with properties unique,
Boron's charm is something you cannot critique.
Its bright crystalline structure, like diamonds so pure,
Reflects its versatility, strong and secure.
From the depths of the Earth, it's abundantly found,
In minerals and compounds, beneath the ground.
Boron, the builder, with a keen eye for bonds,
Forms connections with elements, like magic responds.

With three valence electrons, it seeks to unite,
Creating compounds, with powers so bright.
   Borates, borides, and boron nitride,
In their presence, innovation takes stride.
From detergents to ceramics, and so much more,
Boron's contributions, we simply adore.
   But its true elegance lies in its isotopes' might,
Boron-10 and Boron-11, shining so bright.
In nuclear reactions, they play a key role,
Harnessing energy, with a cosmic control.
   The boron flame, a vibrant green hue,
Lights up the night sky, with a mystical view.
A testament to boron's luminescent grace,
A spectacle that leaves us in a state of embrace.
   So let us celebrate Boron, the element divine,
With its atomic structure, so intricate and fine.
A symbol of progress and scientific endeavor,
Boron, the catalyst, we shall cherish forever.

TWO

ELEMENT OF MIGHT

In the realm of elements, Boron shines bright,
A versatile gem, a scientific delight.
With atomic number five, it makes its mark,
A symbol of progress, a spark in the dark.
Found in minerals, compounds, and ores,
Boron whispers secrets, it silently explores.
A bridge between metals and nonmetals it creates,
Building connections, opening new gates.
Isotopes of Boron, with a secret to unveil,
In nuclear reactions, their stories they tell.
From B-10 to B-11, they dance in the core,
Unleashing energy, unearthing much more.
Oh, the mesmerizing boron flame,
A vivid green hue, a sight to acclaim.
An ethereal glow, a scientific show,
Boron's presence, a spectacle to know.

From the depths of the Earth to the sky above,
Boron whispers of knowledge, of progress and love.
A catalyst, a conductor, a trailblazer in its own right,
Boron dances with atoms, bringing science to light.
So let us celebrate this element of might,
Boron, a symbol of progress, shining ever so bright.
With its unique properties, it paves the way,
For a future of discovery, where science will sway.

THREE

REACHING FOR THE SKY

In the realm of elements, Boron shines,
A gem of chemistry, a marvel divine.
With atomic number five, it takes its place,
A silent warrior, with elegance and grace.

Boron, the guardian of our earthly soil,
With strength and resilience, it never recoils.
Its structure, unique, a testament to its might,
A three-dimensional web, holding atoms tight.

In compounds, Boron dances with the stars,
Creating hues of green, like emerald memoirs.
The borates, a symphony of beauty and grace,
In minerals and gems, they leave their trace.

Boron, the architect of life's blueprint,
Essential for plants, a vital recruit.

It helps form cell walls, lending strength and support,
A guardian angel, nature's consort.
From the deserts to the oceans, Boron prevails,
Its versatility, a testament that never fails.
From medicine to technology, it finds its way,
Contributing to progress day by day.
Oh, Boron, your magic we cannot deny,
A bridge between worlds, reaching for the sky.
In the realm of elements, you hold your own,
A masterpiece of nature, forever known.

FOUR

MAGNIFICENT STAR

In the realm of atoms, a luminary gleams,
Boron, the element of extraordinary dreams.
With six protons and a cosmic allure,
It dances through the universe, pure and secure.
    A catalyst of change, a pioneer of might,
Boron ignites the flame of scientific light.
Its valiant electrons, in an orbit they reside,
Creating bonds that nature could never hide.
    In the depths of the Earth, Boron finds its home,
Where minerals and crystals freely roam.
In borax lakes, a spectacle unfolds,
A testament to Boron's secrets yet untold.
    From the glass industry to medicine's grace,
Boron's touch leaves an indelible trace.
Fiber optics and ceramics, it lends its hand,
Advancing technology across the land.

In mazes of chemistry, Boron plays its part,
A puzzle piece that fits with a masterful art.
From boranes to borates, a symphony it weaves,
Unraveling secrets that science retrieves.
Oh, Boron, you shine with a cosmic allure,
A treasure of the Earth, steadfast and pure.
In laboratories and nature's embrace,
You leave your mark with elegance and grace.
So let us celebrate this element so grand,
A guardian in nature, a guiding hand.
Boron, the versatile, the magnificent star,
Forever illuminating, no matter how far.

FIVE

BORON SHINES

In the depths of the periodic table's realm,
A humble element, Boron, takes the helm.
With an atomic number of five, it resides,
A versatile compound, where progress abides.
  Boron, the builder of compounds so grand,
From borax to boric acid, at its command.
In glass and ceramics, it lends its grace,
Strengthening structures, enhancing their embrace.
  From steel to sunscreen, it plays a role,
Creating alloys and protecting the soul.
Its isotopes, a beacon in nuclear research,
Unraveling mysteries, advancing our perch.
  In the world of chemistry, Boron shines,
Its presence felt in countless designs.
A catalyst, a flame, a light in the dark,
Boron, the element that leaves its mark.

SIX

WONDROUS ELEMENT

In the realm of chemistry, Boron shines,
A versatile element, with powers divine.
With an atomic number of five, it stands proud,
An ally to nature, both silent and loud.

Boron, oh Boron, you nurture the land,
Helping plants grow, with a gentle hand.
In bleaches and soaps, you play your part,
Cleaning and purifying, with a caring heart.

With just two isotopes, you're simple yet grand,
Boron-10 and Boron-11, a steadfast band.
Your contributions, so vast and profound,
In science and industry, you're always around.

Boron, the element, so unique and rare,
Inventing new materials, beyond compare.
Your properties, magical, they never cease,
From borates to borides, a wonder, a masterpiece.

So let us celebrate Boron, this wondrous element,
A symbol of innovation, a true testament.
In the world of chemistry, you'll forever stay,
Boron, oh Boron, our gratitude we convey.

SEVEN

BORON'S CONTRIBUTIONS

Boron, a mineral with many forms,
An element that defies the norms.
From green gems to powders white,
Its diversity is quite a sight.
Its isotopes have many uses,
In medicine and in fuses.
And let us not forget its role,
In strengthening bones, a vital goal.
But Boron's beauty goes beyond,
Its practical uses we rely upon.
For when it's burned with a flame,
It glows with a luminescent fame.
And in science, it's played its part,
In advancing knowledge with its heart.
From chemists to physicists alike,

Boron's properties they do spike.
So let us celebrate this element rare,
For all the ways it does compare.
From nature to industry and more,
Boron's contributions we do adore.

EIGHT

STRENGTH AND GRACE

In the realm of chemistry, a tale unfolds,
Of an element so unique, its story untold.
Boron, a marvel, with secrets to share,
A shimmering essence, beyond compare.
Within the Earth's crust, it silently dwells,
A hidden gem, where beauty compels.
Strengthening bones, it lends a hand,
With Boron's touch, a sturdy frame withstands.
Luminescent in nature, it radiates light,
A spectacle of colors, shining so bright.
In crystals and compounds, its brilliance resides,
A dance of electrons, where wonder abides.
Boron, a symbol of strength and grace,
In chemistry's embrace, it finds its rightful place.

A puzzle piece, completing the grand design,
Unveiling the mysteries, both yours and mine.

NINE

TALE TO BEHOLD

In the realm of elements, a star is born,
A mighty force, a symbol to adorn.
Boron, the chemist's mysterious child,
With secrets and wonders, yet to be compiled.
   A catalyst of progress, it does bestow,
Advancing technology, with each new row.
In semiconductors, it finds its place,
Boosting conductivity with elegant grace.
   From compounds to clusters, Boron's art,
Creating structures, strong from the start.
Its presence enhances, both near and far,
From alloys to ceramics, it raises the bar.
   A versatile element, with talents untold,
Boron's allure, a tale to behold.
In chemistry's dance, it takes its stance,
A vital player, in every circumstance.

TEN

AIRCRAFT TO TURBINES

In the realm of elements, Boron is a star,
With its atomic number shining afar.
A versatile element, it holds many a role,
Strengthening structures, playing a vital role.
In medicine, Boron finds its way,
With compounds that heal, it saves the day.
From arthritis to cancer, it lends a hand,
Aiding the sick, a remedy so grand.
In industry, Boron's uses are vast,
Creating alloys, making metals last.
From aircraft to turbines, it lends its might,
Sturdy and strong, ensuring things take flight.
In science, Boron expands our knowledge,
Its isotopes studied, our minds acknowledge.

From nuclear reactions to neutron detection,
Unraveling mysteries, a scientific connection.
    So let's raise a glass to this wondrous element,
Boron, the versatile, its impact evident.
From medicine to industry, science to art,
Boron, the unsung hero, playing its part.

ELEVEN

RADIANCE TOO

In the realm of science, a tale unfolds,
Of an element rare, with secrets untold.
Boron, the chemist's precious delight,
A gem in the periodic table's light.
　　In medicine's domain, Boron finds its place,
A catalyst for health, with grace and grace.
From cancer treatments to arthritis relief,
Its healing touch brings solace, beyond belief.
　　Oh, Boron, the strength you lend to our bones,
A guardian, a protector, as nature intones.
With calcium, you dance, in harmony's sway,
Building fortresses of strength, day by day.
　　But it's not just strength that you possess,
For your luminescent nature, we are truly impressed.
In crystals and compounds, you shimmer and glow,
A radiant beauty, for all to behold.

So, let us celebrate Boron, the element divine,
A marvel of nature, in its design.
From medicine to strength, and radiance too,
In chemistry's embrace, you shine through.

TWELVE

NEVER BE TAME

Boron, a metalloid with a curious name,
Not quite metal, not gas, nor a flame.
A versatile element, with uses galore,
From space shuttles to ceramics, it's at the core.
A luminescent hue, it can emit,
When bombarded with particles, it doesn't quit.
A brilliant light, in a range of shades,
Boron's properties, science has praised.
It's in the catalysts, that make our fuel,
And in agriculture, it's a crucial tool.
In cosmetics, it keeps us looking fine,
And in energy production, it's a sign.
A healing element, it's been known to cure,
And in science and industry, it's secure.
Boron, a metalloid with a curious name,
Its impact on the world will never be tame.

THIRTEEN

ELEMENT GRAND

In the realm of science, Boron stands tall,
A versatile element, admired by all.
Its electrons dance in a delicate array,
Unveiling secrets in a molecular ballet.
From technology's grasp, Boron takes flight,
In transistors and semiconductors, shining bright.
Its presence empowers the circuits we weave,
A symphony of electrons, with harmony conceived.
In industries diverse, Boron finds its place,
Creating alloys with strength and grace.
From steel to ceramics, it lends its might,
Enhancing materials, sturdy and tight.
But Boron's powers stretch beyond the mundane,
Its healing touch, a gift to sustain.
In medicine's realm, it offers its hand,
Reducing inflammation, a curative band.

So let us honor Boron, this element grand,
With its scientific wonders, forever in demand.
From technology's realm to healing's embrace,
Boron, a marvel, leaving none in its trace.

FOURTEEN

BORON, OH BORON

In industries, Boron finds its place,
Enhancing products with its trace.
From glass to ceramics, it lends a hand,
Strengthening materials, oh so grand.

In medicine, Boron shows its might,
With healing properties, shining bright.
It fights inflammation, eases the pain,
A remedy we can't disdain.

In technology, Boron takes the lead,
In semiconductors, it plants the seed.
Transistors thrive with Boron's might,
Advancing our world, day and night.

So let us celebrate this element true,
Boron, oh Boron, we honor you.
From industry to healing, you play a part,
Enriching our lives, a work of art.

FIFTEEN

TECHNOLOGY TO ART

In realms of chemistry, a gem is found,
A mighty element, Boron renowned.
With atomic number five, it stands tall,
A versatile element, admired by all.

In industry, Boron plays a key role,
Its uses varied, for it has many a goal.
In glassmaking, it lends strength and clarity,
And in steel production, it aids durability.

But Boron's wonders do not end there,
For in medicine, it offers healing care.
From arthritis to cancer, it fights the fight,
Easing pain, bringing hope, shining bright.

In technology's realm, Boron takes flight,
As a dopant in silicon, it ignites,
The power of transistors, the magic of chips,
Enabling our devices, with each tiny blip.

So let us celebrate this element divine,
Boron, a treasure, in every field it shines.
From industry to health, technology to art,
Its contributions leave an everlasting mark.

SIXTEEN

ENHANCING DURABILITY

In the realm of science, a gem so bright,
Boron emerges with its dazzling light.
A versatile element, it knows no bounds,
In medicine and industry, its prowess resounds.

In the realm of healing, Boron takes its stand,
A guardian angel, lending a healing hand.
With its antiviral powers, it fights the fight,
Boosting immunity, a shining knight.

In the realm of strength, Boron stands tall,
Reinforcing materials, one and all.
From steel to ceramics, it lends its might,
Enhancing durability, a warrior of the night.

In the realm of knowledge, Boron unveils,
Unraveling mysteries, its brilliance prevails.

In neutron capture, it shines with grace,
Advancing scientific frontiers, leaving a trace.
    Boron, the element of wonders untold,
A chameleon of elements, so bold.
From medicine to industry, it paves the way,
A beacon of possibilities, every single day.

SEVENTEEN

HEALING POWERS FLARE

In the realm of elements, Boron shines bright,
A versatile gem, with powers to ignite.
From the depths of Earth, its beauty unfurls,
With atomic prowess, it conquers the world.

In industries vast, Boron takes the lead,
Its uses diverse, fulfilling every need.
As a catalyst, it sparks reactions anew,
Unleashing potential, creating breakthroughs.

In glassmaking, Boron weaves its magic spell,
Enhancing strength, making structures excel.
From test tubes to fiber optics, it's found,
Boron's touch, in every corner, profound.

But Boron's wonders do not end there,
For within its grasp, healing powers flare.

In medicine's realm, it finds its place,
Fighting diseases, with elegance and grace.
    It strengthens bones, with its radiant might,
A guardian of health, in the darkest of night.
With Boron's touch, ailments are eased,
A testament to its nature, forever pleased.
    So let us celebrate this element divine,
Boron, the star, in science's grand design.
From industry to medicine, it holds the key,
A symbol of progress, for all to see.

EIGHTEEN

PRESENCE RESOUNDS

In the realm of industries, Boron reigns,
With versatility, its power it claims.
From body armor strong, to cosmetics sublime,
Insecticides and nuclear plants, it's a prime.
Ancient Egyptians, in mummification's art,
Used Boron's properties, playing their part.
Revitalizing olive trees, Greece and Spain,
Borates brought life to the land again.
But Boron's reach extends beyond these bounds,
In healing medicine, its presence resounds.
From strengthening bones to treating arthritis,
It aids in building muscles, enhancing our wits.
So let us celebrate this element true,
With Boron's wonders, there's much to pursue.
In industries and health, its value we see,
Boron, a marvel, forever shall it be.

NINETEEN

SCIENTIFIC INSIGHT

In industries vast, Boron plays its part,
A versatile element with a creative heart.
Used in glassmaking, it lends strength and shine,
In detergents and ceramics, its presence does define.

In medicine's realm, Boron finds its grace,
A healer it becomes in the human space.
Used to treat arthritis, it eases the pain,
And against cancerous cells, it fights the bane.

In technology's realm, Boron does excel,
As a dopant in semiconductors, it casts its spell.
In magnets and superconductors, it shows its might,
Pushing the boundaries of scientific insight.

Boron, oh Boron, an element divine,
With properties unique and powers so fine.
From industry to medicine, you shine bright,
A testament to chemistry's wondrous might.

TWENTY

HIGH DEMAND

In the realm of elements, Boron stands,
With a beauty and strength that truly commands.
A versatile gem, so unique and rare,
With wonders to offer beyond compare.
   In glassmaking's realm, it finds its place,
Enhancing the structure with its grace.
From windows to lenses, it lends its might,
Making visions clearer, shining so bright.
   In medicine's domain, Boron prevails,
With healing powers, it never fails.
Fighting diseases, it takes a stand,
Bringing hope and health to every land.
   In technology's world, it takes the lead,
Powering devices with lightning speed.
From semiconductors to superconductors,
Boron's advancements, the future ushers.

With strength and resilience, it fortifies,
Materials that withstand the test of time.
From metals to ceramics, it imparts,
Sturdiness and durability, a work of art.

In scientific frontiers, it expands,
Unraveling mysteries with its helping hands.
From catalysts to compounds, it aids the way,
Advancing knowledge, day by day.

So, let us celebrate this element grand,
With its many uses, it's in high demand.
Boron, the powerhouse of endless might,
Guiding us towards a brighter light.

TWENTY-ONE

WORLD OF DISRUPTORS

In the realm of elements, a jewel so rare,
Boron, the marvel, beyond compare.
A versatile element, with secrets untold,
Its wonders enchanting, a story unfold.

In glassmaking, Boron is a guiding light,
Adding strength and beauty, shining so bright.
From windows to mirrors, it lends its grace,
Transforming sand into a delicate embrace.

In steel production, Boron takes the lead,
Bestowing strength to meet every need.
With its mighty hand, it forges the way,
Creating alloys that never sway.

In medicine, Boron's healing touch is found,
Fighting diseases, its power unbound.

From cancer treatments to bone repair,
It brings hope and healing, beyond compare.
    In technology's realm, Boron takes flight,
Powering devices, with all its might.
From semiconductors to superconductors,
It fuels innovation, a world of disruptors.
    In every field, Boron leaves its mark,
A versatile element, shining in the dark.
With its unique properties, it paves the way,
Unleashing progress, day after day.

TWENTY-TWO

ACROSS EVERY LAND

In the realm of elements, Boron stands tall,
A symbol of strength, it never does fall.
With atomic number five, it holds its ground,
A warrior in nature, forever renowned.
Boron, the healer, with powers untold,
In medicine's realm, its worth is solid gold.
Its isotopes fight cancer, a battle so fierce,
A remedy for ailments, its touch so sincere.
In industries vast, Boron plays a key role,
From glassmaking's art to ceramics' soul.
Its presence enhances, its magic unfolds,
Creating wonders, as its story is told.
In technology's realm, Boron takes flight,
With semiconductors, it guides us right.
Superconductors it aids, in their quest for more,
Pushing boundaries, unlocking every door.

Fortifying materials, Boron's might is seen,
Enhancing their strength, like a dream within a dream.
Advancements in science owe Boron their debt,
A catalyst for progress, we shall never forget.
So let us celebrate this element true,
Its versatility, its impact, it's all that we do.
From steel production to medicines so grand,
Boron's legacy, across every land.

TWENTY-THREE

INSPIRING US ALL

In the realm of elements, Boron does reside,
A versatile soul with much to provide.
From glassmakers' dreams to detergents' tide,
Boron's touch weaves magic far and wide.

In the land of ceramics, Boron takes its place,
Strengthening structures with its mighty embrace.
With heat and pressure, it lends a helping hand,
Crafting vessels sturdy, enduring, and grand.

But Boron's talents don't stop there,
In medicine's realm, it shows its care.
As a healer, it aids in the fight,
Against ailments and diseases, day and night.

Technology, too, finds solace in Boron's might,
In semiconductors, it dances in the light.
Superconductors sing to its tune,
Unlocking new frontiers, reaching the moon.

Oh Boron, the backbone of steel's creation,
Forging strength, resilience, and elation.
In the heart of industry, you hold your sway,
Building structures that withstand, come what may.
    And in the realm of healing, you lend your grace,
Easing pain, bringing solace to every case.
From arthritis to cancer, you fight the fight,
A guardian of health, shining ever so bright.
    From glass to ceramics, from medicine to tech,
Boron's versatility, we cannot neglect.
A wondrous element, diverse and profound,
In every field, its worth is renowned.
    So let us celebrate Boron's embrace,
Its impact across fields, its unyielding grace.
For in the world of elements, it stands tall,
A powerhouse of wonder, inspiring us all.

TWENTY-FOUR

BEYOND THE LAB'S DOOR

In the realm of elements, Boron shines bright,
A versatile gem, a chemical delight.
From glassmaking to detergents, it finds its way,
With uses diverse, in every sphere it holds sway.

In the world of glass, where beauty takes form,
Boron lends its strength, a secret to transform.
With its presence, windows gleam with clarity,
A touch of Boron, a touch of transparency.

In detergents, it fights against stubborn stains,
A cleansing agent, where dirt and grime wanes.
Boron's power, in every soap and cleaner,
Making chores easier, a true hygiene enabler.

Ceramics too, owe a debt to this element,
With Boron's touch, they gain strength and temperament.

From tiles to pottery, it adds resilience and might,
A touch of Boron, making ceramics shine bright.
Medicine, too, finds Boron's aid,
In cancer research, a path it has laid.
With its unique properties, it fights the fight,
A beacon of hope, in the darkest of night.
Technology, a realm where Boron thrives,
In semiconductors, it helps electrons strive.
From computer chips to solar cells that gleam,
Boron's role, a key in the technological dream.
In scientific research, it plays a crucial part,
As a catalyst, it ignites discoveries, a work of art.
Boron's contributions, a testament profound,
Advancing knowledge, with each scientific bound.
So let us celebrate Boron, this element grand,
With its myriad uses, it leaves us in awe, unplanned.
From industry to medicine, and beyond the lab's door,
Boron's impact shines, forevermore.

TWENTY-FIVE

ENDLESS MAZE

In the realm of elements, a star takes its place,
Boron, the mighty, with elegance and grace.
A chameleon of sorts, it dazzles and glows,
With secrets to share that few others know.
In industry's hands, it finds its true might,
A warrior, a hero, in the heat of the fight.
From steel to ceramics, it strengthens them all,
With resilience and power, it'll never fall.
In medicine's realm, Boron lends a hand,
A healer, a mender, a guardian so grand.
From cancer treatments to bone's embrace,
It offers hope and solace, in life's hardest race.
In scientific research, it's a beacon of light,
Unraveling mysteries, like a scientist's delight.
From catalysts to compounds, it dances and weaves,

Creating new wonders, with each experiment conceived.

In technology's realm, it surges ahead,
An innovator, a disruptor, where possibilities spread.
From semiconductors to superconductors' dream,
It pushes the boundaries, like a futuristic stream.

Oh, Boron, you captivate, with your versatile ways,
A marvel, a genius, in our world's endless maze.
Your strength and adaptability, a wonder to behold,
Leaving us in awe, as your stories are told.

TWENTY-SIX

PROPERTIES SO DIVERSE

Boron, oh Boron, a versatile element,
In the periodic table, you're a true testament.
In steel production, you play a vital role,
Making it stronger, harder, and more whole.
Medicine and technology, you impact them both,
In nuclear reactors, you're a crucial growth.
Advancing scientific research, you're truly unique,
Properties so diverse, you're a scientist's mystique.
From your use in laundry detergent to rocket fuel,
Your impact on industry is truly surreal.
A rare earth element, you're a treasure,
Making the world a better place, beyond measure.
Boron, oh Boron, we salute your innovation,
Your versatility and impact, beyond our imagination.

TWENTY-SEVEN

DAZZLING LIGHT

In the depths of steel's fiery blaze,
Boron's secret dance, a hidden phase.
With strength and grace, it weaves its role,
In steel's creation, a vital soul.
A catalyst within the molten sea,
Boron's touch brings strength with glee.
For in its presence, steel transforms,
To sturdy structures, it conforms.
But Boron's reach goes far beyond,
In medicine's realm, a bond it's spawned.
From cancer treatments to bone repair,
Boron's healing touch, beyond compare.
And in the realm of technology's might,
Boron shines with a dazzling light.
In semiconductors, it finds its place,
Enhancing circuits with its trace.

So let us marvel at Boron's might,
From steel to medicine, a guiding light.
In technology's embrace, it thrives,
A versatile element that forever strives.

TWENTY-EIGHT

VAST AND FINE

In the realm of elements, Boron stands tall,
A versatile beauty, a wonder for all.
In industry, medicine, and technology's embrace,
Boron shines brightly with its ethereal grace.

In the world of steel, it strengthens the core,
Creating alloys that are sturdy and pure.
With Boron's touch, metals become strong,
Defying the forces that try to do wrong.

In medicine's realm, Boron finds its way,
Treating osteoarthritis, a savior each day.
With its healing touch, it eases the pain,
Restoring mobility, like a gentle rain.

In the realm of technology, Boron takes flight,
Enhancing semiconductors, a beacon of light.
With its electron-hungry ways, it paves the path,
Accelerating progress, avoiding any aftermath.

Oh, Boron, you catalyst of endless possibility,
From industry to medicine, you create agility.
Your presence, so subtle, yet so profound,
A building block for progress, forever renowned.
So let us celebrate this element divine,
For its contribution, so vast and fine.
Boron, a marvel, in its own unique way,
A testament to chemistry's power, we must say.

TWENTY-NINE

TOUCH OF GRACE

In the realm of Boron, a tale unfolds,
A dance of atoms, a story untold.
A metalloid, with a touch of grace,
Boron, the element, takes its place.
In steel's fiery forge, Boron finds its might,
Strengthening the metal, making it tight.
Hardening the structure, with a subtle touch,
Boron's presence, it means so much.
In medicine's realm, Boron plays a role,
A catalyst for life, it takes its toll.
From the lab to the clinic, it lends a hand,
Fighting diseases, a noble command.
In technology's realm, Boron takes flight,
Powering devices, shining so bright.
From the silicon chips to the glass displays,
Boron's magic, it never betrays.

So, let us celebrate this element of might,
Boron's wonders, shining so bright.
In steel, medicine, and technology's embrace,
Boron leaves its mark, with elegance and grace.

THIRTY

ADVANCING TECHNOLOGY

Boron, a miracle element so pure,
Its properties, so unique, hard to ignore.
Its versatility knows no bounds,
Its impact in various fields astounds.
    In strengthening structures, it's a pro,
In treating osteoarthritis, it's a go.
In enhancing semiconductors, it's a must,
In making laundry detergents, it's a trust.
    Boron, a boon for metallurgy,
In hardening metal, it's a prodigy.
In fighting diseases, it's a savior,
In powering devices, it's a generator.
    Boron, a gem in the world of science,
In fortifying structures, it's a reliance.

In relieving pain, it's a respite,
In advancing technology, it's a delight.
    Boron, a wonder element so pure,
Its significance, will forever endure.

THIRTY-ONE

INDELIBLE MARK

In the realm of elements, let Boron rise,
A versatile gem, a chemical prize.
With atomic number five, it claims its place,
Unveiling the wonders of its atomic space.
    In industry's embrace, Boron finds its might,
Creating alloys, with metals shining bright.
Stronger than steel, its strength will endure,
Building foundations that stand tall and secure.
    In medicine's realm, Boron finds its way,
Treating osteoarthritis, easing pain's sway.
With supplements, it aids bones' resilience,
Bringing relief, a gift of its brilliance.
    In technology's realm, Boron takes the stage,
Enhancing semiconductors, the digital age.
With its doping prowess, it unlocks the gates,
Powering devices, where innovation awaits.

In laundry's domain, Boron lends a hand,
Making detergents work, as stains are banned.
It softens water, fights dirt with its might,
Leaving fabrics clean, in a world of white.

Oh Boron, a marvel, a treasure untold,
Your impact on science, we can't withhold.
From industry to medicine, technology's rise,
You've left an indelible mark, beneath the skies.

So let us celebrate, this element grand,
In laboratories, where science expands.
For Boron, dear Boron, forever we'll know,
Your significance, your legacy, will forever glow.

THIRTY-TWO

INDUSTRY TO MEDICINE

In realms of science, Boron holds its might,
A versatile element, shining so bright.
From industry to medicine, its impact profound,
A catalyst of progress, in various grounds.
　　In steel's creation, Boron plays a role,
Strengthening structures, making them whole.
With carbon and Boron, a powerful blend,
Transforming alloys, their strength to extend.
　　In medicine's realm, Boron finds its place,
Treating osteoarthritis with gentle grace.
Relieving the pain, healing the bones,
Boron's touch, a remedy shown.
　　In technology's realm, Boron takes flight,
Enhancing semiconductors, with pure delight.

With Boron doping, electrons flow,
Creating devices, where dreams can grow.
   Boron, the jewel in metallurgy's crown,
Aiding in shaping, structures renowned.
From aircraft to automobiles, strong and true,
Boron's presence, a marvel to view.
   In disease treatment, Boron lends its hand,
Fighting cancer cells, a battle so grand.
With Boron neutron capture, a ray of hope,
Destroying tumors, a lifesaving scope.
   In the digital age, Boron takes command,
Powering devices, with a steady hand.
In batteries and capacitors, it plays its part,
Fueling our gadgets, igniting the spark.
   In laundry detergents, Boron finds its way,
Boosting cleaning power, day by day.
Softening water, removing the grime,
Boron's touch, making clothes sublime.
   Oh, Boron, the wonder of science's domain,
With endless possibilities, you shall reign.
From industry to medicine, technology too,
Boron's magic, forever shining through.

THIRTY-THREE

CATALYST OF PROGRESS

In the realm of elements, Boron shines so bright,
A catalyst of change, a beacon of light.
With six protons and five electrons it stands,
A symbol of strength, in nature's own hands.

In structures it strengthens, like a steadfast friend,
Binding atoms together, it won't ever bend.
In alloys and ceramics, its power resides,
Enhancing the materials that our world provides.

But Boron's reach goes beyond mere construction,
In medicine's realm, it finds its own junction.
For osteoarthritis, it offers relief,
Reducing inflammation, mending the grief.

And in the realm of technology's domain,
Boron takes center stage, it's not in vain.

As a dopant in semiconductors, it excels,
Enhancing conductivity, ringing the bells.
    Oh, Boron, you're unique, a versatile mate,
With each passing day, new wonders you create.
From strengthening structures to healing the ill,
In every field, your potential, it feels.
    So let us raise a glass to Boron's grand role,
A catalyst of progress, a chemical soul.
In every corner of science, it leaves its mark,
Boron, the element, a true shining spark.

THIRTY-FOUR

UNRAVELING MYSTERIES

In the realm of elements, Boron holds its might,
A silent warrior, hidden in plain sight.
With strength and resilience, it strengthens structures,
Unyielding, unbreakable, like nature's sculptures.
From ancient times to the present day,
Boron's secrets, science seeks to convey.
In osteoarthritis, it lends a healing hand,
Easing pain, bringing relief to the land.
In technology's realm, it plays a vital role,
Powering devices with an electric control.
Semiconductors thrive on Boron's might,
Enhancing conductivity, shining bright.
Boron, a guardian against the cancerous foe,
Fighting malignant cells, a powerful blow.

With precision and grace, it seeks to destroy,
The scourge of disease, a symbol of joy.
   Inflammation, it tames with its gentle touch,
Reducing the fire that hurts so much.
In osteoarthritis, it brings a soothing balm,
Restoring mobility, a healing calm.
   Boron, a hero in the world of science,
Forging new pathways with each compliance.
A versatile element, with secrets untold,
Unraveling mysteries, as the story unfolds.

THIRTY-FIVE

GIFT SO RARE

In the realm of elements, let me sing,
Of Boron, a humble and mighty thing.
With strength and grace, it weaves its way,
Into structures that stand, come what may.
A sturdy backbone, it does provide,
To materials with resilience and pride.
In fibers strong, it finds its place,
Enhancing strength with elegant grace.
But Boron's wonders don't end there,
Its healing touch, a gift so rare.
For those with aching joints and bones,
Osteoarthritis, it gently hones.
And in the world of technology,
Boron's role is a sight to see.
In semiconductors, it takes the lead,
Empowering devices with incredible speed.

So let us celebrate this element true,
With properties that astound and imbue.
Boron, a marvel, both strong and smart,
Forever etching its mark in every part.

THIRTY-SIX

SOURCE OF FASCINATION

In the realm of elements, Boron shines,
A versatile gem with powers so fine.
Metallurgy's friend, it strengthens alloys,
In aerospace and turbines, it brings us joys.

But Boron's magic extends far and wide,
In medicine, it fights diseases with pride.
From cancer cells to arthritis pain,
Boron's touch brings hope, a healing rain.

Advancing technology, Boron leads the way,
Powering devices, with energy to sway.
From batteries to lasers, it sparks innovation,
A catalyst for progress, a source of fascination.

So let us raise a toast to Boron's might,
A chemical marvel, a guiding light.

In metallurgy, medicine, and technology's realm,
Boron, the element that overwhelms.

THIRTY-SEVEN

SEMICONDUCTING GLOW

Boron, oh Boron, a versatile element indeed,
With properties that make it a precious metal to feed
Cancer cells beware, for Boron's neutron capture ther-
apy
Can eradicate you with precision and efficacy
But Boron's powers don't end there, oh no,
For it can also power devices with its semiconduct-
ing glow
And strengthen alloys with its hardening effect
Making them more durable and resistant to defect
So though Boron may seem humble, it is key
In fighting cancer, powering the world, and metallurgy
A true hero in the periodic table's midst
Boron, oh Boron, we sing your praises with bliss.

THIRTY-EIGHT

UNSUNG HERO

In the realm of chemistry, a hero stands tall,
With its atomic number, five, we call,
Boron, the element, so versatile and grand,
A true champion in the periodic table's band.
    In nature's embrace, Boron finds its place,
From the Earth's crust, it emerges with grace,
A humble element, yet mighty in its role,
Unleashing wonders that touch every soul.
    Boron, the guardian, in cancer's dire fight,
A weapon against tumor cells, shining bright,
In targeted therapy, it takes the lead,
Attacking the enemy with precision and speed.
    In the realm of technology, Boron takes flight,
Powering devices with all its might,
Semiconductors, batteries, and much more,
Boron's conductivity, a technological lore.

Its strength and resilience, a metallurgist's dream,
Boron alloys, an unbeatable team,
From spacecraft to sports equipment, it excels,
Endowing strength, where it dwells.
Boron, oh Boron, you're truly divine,
A testament to nature's design,
With your myriad uses, a force to be reckoned,
A hero in chemistry, we beckon.
So let us celebrate this element so rare,
With its atomic structure, beyond compare,
Boron, the unsung hero, we honor today,
In the world of chemistry, forever it shall sway.

ABOUT THE AUTHOR

Walter the Educator is one of the pseudonyms for Walter Anderson. Formally educated in Chemistry, Business, and Education, he is an educator, an author, a diverse entrepreneur, and he is the son of a disabled war veteran. "Walter the Educator" shares his time between educating and creating. He holds interests and owns several creative projects that entertain, enlighten, enhance, and educate, hoping to inspire and motivate you.

Follow, find new works, and stay up to date with Walter the Educator™ at WaltertheEducator.com

Milton Keynes UK
Ingram Content Group UK Ltd.
UKHW020947221123
433051UK00020B/865